A Message from Georgia's First Lady

T.J.'s Discovery is a simple family adventure that confronts a child's fear of the dark with creative activities and explanations. The book engages the five senses to turn fear into confidence. Children can identify and empathize with the character because we all have experienced fear. It is a book that stimulates the imagination while introducing new ideas and vocabulary. Our goal is for each child to take it home and read with a parent.

This book is a teaching tool for parents and caregivers of young children. It offers, in small print, suggestions of activities and explanations of unfamiliar words to stimulate understanding, relevance, imagination, interaction and conversation. My hope in choosing this book is that it will help parents become more confident as they engage their children in the process of learning to read. Brain development and reading proficiency occur by talking and reading to your child at home, and is reinforced by competent instruction in the classroom.

Nathan and I benefitted greatly by having mothers who were trained as primary teachers to help us become proficient readers. We believe parents want to help their children become successful readers and lifelong achievers. I think this book can be a useful tool for teaching the basic skills of engagement. After gaining confidence, we hope your child will enjoy telling the story and reading to you. We hope reading together everyday will become a habit. Practice is important.

Hopefully, the skills gained can be used to help you read other books and to stimulate conversations about your own family's adventures and discoveries. It takes parents, teachers, and the community working together to lay the educational groundwork for academic success. Nathan and I appreciate the public and private partnerships that continue to assist Georgia's most precious resource, her children.

Sandra Deal

Sandra Deal
First Lady of Georgia

How you read with children makes a difference, for a lifetime.

A book can transform a child's life forever. By reading this book at least three times, you help children build language and vocabulary, engage in meaningful conversation, nurture critical thinking, and create powerful, determined learners and problem solvers.

read **3** times

How to transform story time into the ultimate learning experience for each and every child

---

1st READ

FOCUS ON EVENTS

The first time you read, use think-alouds to teach vocabulary, key events, and the story problem. Use voices, expressions, tone and pace to help bring the story to life.

2nd READ

FOCUS ON EMOTIONS

The second time you read, use think-alouds to teach vocabulary and characters' thoughts and feelings related to key events. Remember to use expression in your voice to bring joy to reading.

3rd READ

CHILD TELLS THE STORY

WAY TO GO!

The third time you read, encourage children to tell you about the key events and how they relate to the character's thoughts and feelings. As you read, ask questions such as, "What's happening here?"

Tips for reading:

 Point to words

Point to illustrations to help children understand key vocabulary

 Act out words

Help children understand important vocabulary by acting out these words

 Tell child-friendly definitions

Define key vocabulary using words the children understand

 Use think-alouds

Use think-alouds to help children understand important parts of the story. You can say things like, "I wonder why..." or "She must feel... because..."

Ask open-ended questions

At the end of the story, ask a "how" or "why" question to encourage children to discuss key events and characters' thoughts and feelings related to those events

 Respond

Respond to children using well-formed sentences and key vocabulary from the story

Tie the book to other parts of the day

Plan centers and small group activities connected to the story that encourage children to use vocabulary from the book

 For more information, visit the Cox Campus COX Campus
www.readrightfromthestart.org

Rollins Center *for Language & Literacy* | A Program of the Atlanta Speech School

PAT the Vocabulary (adapted from Lea McGee)

T.J.'s Discovery

Before You Read the Book, Say:

1<u>st</u> read - (Point to cover) This girl must be T.J. I wonder why she is out in the dark forest at night. Let's read and find out.

2<u>nd</u> read - I remember from last time that T.J. was afraid of the dark at first. I wonder why T.J. felt comfortable in the dark by the end of the book. Let's read and find out.

3<u>rd</u> read - I wonder why T.J.'s dad made shadow puppets with his daughters. Let's read and find out.

By Rollins Center for Language & Literacy at the Atlanta Speech School
Illustrated by Dr. Karinna Riddett-Moore

T.J. <u>stretched</u> her neck to see around
(A – act out stretching your neck)

her classmates. She loved it when

Mrs. Allen read the <u>rabbit book</u>!
(P – point)

1

"Why was the baby rabbit <u>afraid</u> here?" Mrs. Allen
(T – scared)
asked. T.J. raised her hand. "He did not like the dark."

Mrs. Allen <u>nodded</u>. "Exactly. It can be scary
(A – act out nodding head)
for a little animal to be in the dark <u>forest</u>."
(T – a place with many trees, the woods)

2

T.J. furrowed her eyebrows. *She* was going camping
(A – act out furrowing your eyebrows; T – bunched up)   (T – sleeping in a tent outside)
this weekend, in the forest, where it would get *dark.*
(T – woods, place with many trees)

Mrs. Allen interrupted her thoughts
(T – stopped T.J. while she was thinking)
saying, "But in the end, the rabbit

loved the forest. Think about that

this weekend and then come back

and tell me why on Monday."

On the bus ride home, T.J. kept

thinking about the forest.

Use think-alouds:

On the bus ride home T.J. is thinking about the baby rabbit and how scary the forest was with all those animals. She's probably thinking, "I'm so worried about going camping in the dark."

She could not see why the rabbit would ever love such a dark, scary place.

6

At home, while Mom, Daddy, and Jessica packed

their <u>supplies</u> into the car, T.J. sat next to her
(T – things they would need)

<u>backpack</u>. She was <u>reluctant</u> to go camping.
    (P – point)   (T – not sure)

"Oh Teddy, *you* are not <u>afraid</u> of the dark," she
(A – act out by biting your nails; T – scared)
whispered. She was glad Teddy was coming with her.

Use *think-alouds*:

I'm thinking T.J. is nervous about the camping trip. She is unsure about what will happen in the forest.

8

At the <u>campsite</u>, T.J. and
(T – place where you go camping)
Jessica helped <u>pitch</u> the
(T – set up)
<u>tent</u> by pushing the
(P – point)
poles through the loops.

Mom and Daddy

started a <u>campfire</u>.
(P – point)

That evening the family roasted

marshmallows for <u>s'mores</u> around the
(T – a special treat made of graham crackers, roasted marshmallows, and chocolate)

campfire. As the sun began to set, T.J. watched

the light <u>disappear</u> through
(T – go away)

the trees and her stomach felt

shaky and tight.

11

Use think-alouds:

The sun is setting. T.J. is getting concerned and thinking, "The sun is going down. I'm afraid of the dark. I don't want to sleep in the dark."

12

At bedtime, T.J. put on her
pajamas and then asked, "Mom,
can we leave the <u>lantern</u> on, please?"
(P – point)

13

Mom patted T.J.'s back. "You do not need to be afraid.

I know it's dark, but <u>listen</u>. The only things out there
(A – act out by placing hand to ear)

in the woods tonight are <u>crickets</u> chirping, <u>owls</u> hooting,
(P – point)   (P – point)

<u>whippoorwills</u> calling, and <u>frogs</u> croaking. Those are all
(P – point)   (P – point)

friendly animals," she <u>soothed</u>.
(T – tried to make T.J. feel better)

T.J. listened. Mom was right.

Those were nice sounds.

14

But still... the night was getting darker

and darker. T.J. <u>squeezed</u> Teddy tight and
(A – act out squeezing; T- held tightly)

<u>gulped</u>. "Maybe I could just leave my little
(A – act out gulped; T – swallowed hard)

flashlight on," T.J. whispered.

Use think-alouds:

T.J.'s mom tried to comfort her, but she's noticing that it's getting very dark outside. I think she's squeezing teddy to help her feel better.

"Aw, sweetheart," Daddy <u>reassured</u>, "You are braver
(T – told her it was okay)
than you think. Plus, let me show you something."

Use think-alouds:

I'm thinking that Daddy made those shadow puppets to help comfort T.J. to help make her feel better. Doing something fun to get our mind off our fear can help us overcome, or get over, it.

And with that, Daddy aimed T.J.'s flashlight at the side of the tent. Then he <u>connected</u> his thumbs together and
(T – hooked)

flapped his hands in front of the light. There, on the tent wall, an <u>owl</u> appeared! Daddy hooted, "Hoo, hoo!" and Jessica
(P – point)

and T.J. giggled with glee. "Do it again!" they squealed.

"See, sweetie, the dark is not so bad. You can't make <u>shadow</u>
(T – the dark shape you make when you block light)

puppets without it!" Daddy said.

"Now, it is bedtime. Are you ready to turn off your flashlight?" T.J. nodded. She was still a little <u>nervous</u> about the dark, but her mind

(T – not sure)

was on the little rabbit.

She wondered if there might be a nervous rabbit right here in this forest, cuddled up with its family just like her. Maybe she could even see one outside.

She <u>hesitantly</u> looked out
(T – slowly and carefully)
of the tent. T.J. expected the
forest outside to look dark
and <u>ominous</u>.
(T – scary)

Use think-alouds:

Observing nature seems to make her feel calm. She's probably thinking, "This isn't as scary as I thought it would be." Her observation in the dark is helping her overcome her fear.

She took in a <u>deep</u> <u>breath</u>. She could
(A – act out deep breath)
smell the rich, <u>damp</u> earth and the
(T – a little wet)
<u>leaves</u> and <u>bark</u> from the forest trees.
(P – point)   (T – outside part of a tree)
She felt a gentle breeze across her face.

She heard a whippoorwill <u>calling</u> from
(T – making a sound; A – act out whippoorwill sound)
far away and pictured it singing from

its nest. Even though she didn't see a

rabbit, she pictured one tucked in its

cozy nest with its family.

She looked up. In the dark, she could see feathery white <u>clouds</u> <u>drifting</u> slowly across
(P – point) (T – moving slowly)
the deep blue sky. With the lights off, she <u>discovered</u>
(T – found out)
that she could see bright, brilliant stars <u>twinkling</u>
(T – shining)
above the tree branches—more stars than she had ever seen before!

T.J. smiled.
The dark forest
was not scary after
all. Instead, it was
absolutely beautiful.

24

T.J. snuggled into her sleeping bag. She had

<u>discovered</u> why the rabbit loved the <u>forest</u> so
(T – found out)   (T – the woods)
much. And it turned out that she loved it, too.

25

T.J. couldn't wait until Monday!

After Reading, Ask Open-Ended Questions:

1st read - **Why was T.J. nervous about going camping?** (Possible answers: because she was afraid of the dark; she was concerned and nervous about the dark forest.)

2nd read - **Why did T.J.'s mom help her listen to animals and why did her dad show her how to make shadow puppets?** (Possible answers: because they wanted to comfort her and reassure her that she didn't have to be afraid; they wanted to help her overcome her fear.)

3rd read - **Why can't T.J. wait until Monday?** (Possible answers: she wants to tell her teacher how beautiful the forest is and that rabbit probably loved it because it was beautiful too; she didn't have to be afraid when she was safe with her family.)

Tie the Book to Other Parts of the Day

Activities at home

Each activity addresses one or more of the Georgia Early Learning and Development Standards (GELDS). For more information, go to www.gelds.decal.ga.gov.

- **Create** a tent from sheets and chairs at home. Encourage your child to pretend to go camping. Talk about the supplies you might need (you could even make them from found items—such as a "flashlight" made from an old paper towel roll). You can also talk about the things you might see and do while camping.
  GELDS: APL4, CLL2
- **Read** other books about shadows with your child. You can find many of these at your local library. Here are some examples: Moonbear's Shadow by Frank Asch, Shadows & Reflections by Tana Hoban, & What Makes a Shadow by Clyde Bulla and June Otani. GELDS: CLL5
- **Make** s'mores in your microwave. Talk about the taste, texture, and temperature of the ingredients. GELDS: PDM4, SC1
- **Observe** outside or inside by a window. Encourage your child to observe nature– the plants, animals, and world around us. Talk about what you both hear, see, smell, and feel outside. Does being outside and observing nature make you feel calm and peaceful like it did for T.J.? Talk about other things that help you feel calm when you might be nervous or anxious (ex: taking a deep breath, going for a walk, singing a favorite song). GELDS: SC3, SED2, PDM4
- **Share** your own stories. Tell your child about a situation when you were a child and you felt scared or spent some time outside. Tell him or her your favorite parts and recreate your childhood memories through stories. GELDS: CLL1
- **Encourage** your child to tell this story to friends, siblings, or stuffed animals. Tell your child how impressed you are that he or she remembers so much of the story. Talk about how proud you are that he or she can be the storyteller now.
  GELDS: CLL8, SED1
- **Go Camping!** Visit your backyard or a local park and point out parts of a tree that you might not usually stop and talk about. Show your child the bark, the twigs, the roots, the branches, the leaves, the buds, the flowers, and other things you might find. Talk about how each part of the tree feels and looks. Is it bumpy, smooth, rough, soft, hard, moist, dry? GELDS: SC3, APL2, CLL2

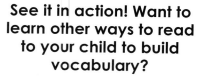

See it in action! Want to learn other ways to read to your child to build vocabulary?

atlantaspeechschool.org/read

Visit your Georgia State Parks! Find more information at www.gastateparks.org

GEORGIA
DEPARTMENT OF NATURAL RESOURCES
STATE PARKS & HISTORIC SITES

Tie the Book to Other Parts of the Day

Activities for the classroom

Each activity addresses one or more of the Georgia Early Learning and Development Standards (GELDS). For more information, go to www.gelds.decal.ga.gov.

- **Read** other books about shadows with your class. Here are some examples: Moonbear's Shadow by Frank Asch, Shadows & Reflections by Tana Hoban, and What Makes a Shadow by Clyde Bulla and June Otani. GELDS: CLL5
- **Use** a flashlight to show your class how to create shadow puppets on a blank wall. Discuss how you move your fingers and hands to make each shape. Talk about how your hands block the light source to create a shadow on the surface of the wall. GELDS: APL2, CPL1
- **Talk** about how shadows are made when we block the light from the sun with our bodies. Outside, use sidewalk chalk to trace your child's shadow on the ground, or just take turns moving and watching your shadows copy what you are doing. GELDS: SC2, PDM6
- **Watch** how animals move and listen to sounds they make. When outside, if you see an insect, bird, or squirrel, point it out to your child. See if your child can imitate the movements and/or sounds you observe. Use new words your child might not know yet like wiggle, chirp, chatter, leap, scamper, and soar to describe what the insects, birds, or squirrels do. GELDS: SC3, APL4, CP2, CR4
- **Write** about nature. Observe animals, insects, and plants outside. Allow your children to create their own stories about what is outside their windows and write down their words on paper. Visit www.readrightfromthestart.org to learn more about emergent writing activities. GELDS: CLL9
- **Encourage** your child to tell this story to friends or take turns in class. Tell your children how impressed you are that they remember so much of the story. Talk about how proud you are that they can be the storytellers now. GELDS: CLL8, SED1

Find more information, training, and planning guides visit readrightfromthestart.org

 Read Right *from the* Start
by the Rollins Center *for* Language & Literacy

This book was created in partnership with

Georgia's
Pre-K Program

PNC

BRIGHT from the START

Georgia Department of Early Care and Learning